Domain 1
Fables and Stories

Domain 2
The Human Body

Domain 3
Different Lands, Similar Stories

Domain 4
Early World Civilizations

Domain 5
Early American Civilizations

Domain 6
Astronomy

Domains 1 - 6
Tell it Again!™ Workbook

Listening & Learning™ Strand
GRADE 1

Amplify learning.

Core Knowledge®

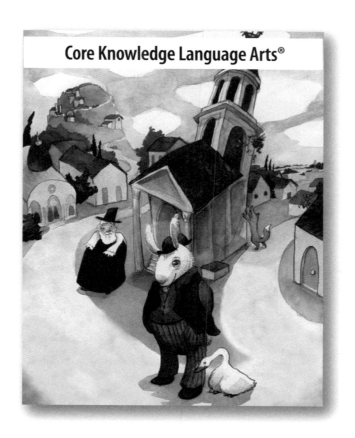

Core Knowledge Language Arts®

Domain 1: Fables and Stories
Tell it Again!™ Workbook

Listening & Learning™ Strand
GRADE 1

Amplify learning.

Core Knowledge®

Dear Family Member,

Today, your child listened to the well-known fable, "The Boy Who Cried Wolf," and learned that fables are short stories that teach a lesson that is called the moral of the story. Over the next several days, your child will also become familiar with the fables, "The Maid and the Milk Pail," "The Goose and the Golden Eggs," "The Dog in the Manger," "The Wolf in Sheep's Clothing," and "The Fox and the Grapes." Some of these fables have animal characters that act like people (personification), which is another characteristic of fables.

Below are some suggestions for activities that you may do at home to continue enjoying the fables heard at school.

1. Character, Setting, and Plot

Talk with your child about the characters, setting, and plot of the fables. Ask questions about the fable such as, "Why did the shepherd boy play a prank and cry, *Wolf! Wolf!*"? Also, make personal connections to the fables with questions such as, "If you often don't tell the truth, will people believe you when you are telling the truth?"

2. Illustrating Fables

Have your child draw or paint a picture of one of the fables and then tell you about it. Again, ask questions to keep your child talking about the fable. Another option is to create a three-part picture that shows the beginning, middle, and end of the fable.

3. Different Versions of Fables

Tell or read to your child different versions of a fable, and talk about how the different versions are the same and how they are different.

4. Sayings and Phrases: Wolf in Sheep's Clothing and Sour Grapes

Your child will learn about these phrases and their meanings. Once your child has heard the fable "The Wolf in Sheep's Clothing," reinforce that the saying means that people are not always whom they appear to be on the outside. On the outside, the wolf looked like a sheep—but he was not. Explain that in the same way, a person can seem very nice on the outside, but may not actually be very nice on the inside. Once your child has heard the fable "The Fox and the Grapes," reinforce that when he couldn't reach the grapes, the fox said, "I didn't want those old grapes anyway. I'm sure they are sour."

Explain that the phrase "sour grapes" describes someone who cannot get what s/he wants, so ends up saying untrue things. Talk with your child again about how these phrases apply to everyday situations.

5. Read Aloud Each Day

It is very important that you read to your child every day. The local library has fables and collections of fables that you can share with your child. A list of books and other relevant resources is attached to this letter. Be sure to talk about the characteristics of each fable—they are short; they have a moral; they use personification—and how the moral applies to you and your child.

Let your child know how much you enjoy hearing about what s/he has learned at school.

Recommended Resources for Fables and Stories

Trade Book List

Fables

1. *Aesop's Fables,* by Jerry Pinkney (Chronicle Books, 2000) ISBN 978-1587170003

2. *Aesop's Fables,* by Beverly Naidoo and illustrated by Piet Grobler (Frances Lincoln Children's Books, 2011) ISBN 978-1847800077

3. *The Boy Who Cried Wolf,* by B.G. Hennessy and illustrated by Boris Kulikov (Simon and Schuster, 2006) ISBN 978-0689874338

4. *The Boy Who Cried Wolf/el Pastorcito Mentiroso: A Retelling of Aesop's Fable/Versión de la fábula de Esopo (Bilingual Edition, Audio Book),* by Eric Blair and illustrated by Dianne Silverman (Capstone Press, 2008) ISBN 978-1404844704

5. *The Classic Treasury of Aesop's Fables (Children's Illustrated Classics),* illustrated by Don Daily (Running Press, 2007) ISBN 978-0762428762

6. *The Fox and the Grapes,* by Mark White and illustrated by Sara Rojo Pérez (Capstone Press, 2008) ISBN 978-1479518562

7. *Fox Tails: Four Fables from Aesop,* by Amy Lowry (Holiday House, 2012) ISBN 978-0823424009

8. *How the Leopard Got His Claws,* by Chinua Achebe and illustrated by Mary GrandPré (Candlewick, 2011) 978-0763648053

9. *The Lion and the Mouse,* retold and illustrated by Bernadette Watts (North-South Books, 2007) ISBN 978-0735821293

10. *Little Cloud and Lady Wind,* by Toni Morrison and Slade Morrison and illustrated by Sean Qualls (Simon & Schuster, 2010) ISBN 978-1416985235

11. *The Tortoise and the Hare,* adapted and illustrated by Janet Stevens (Holiday House, 1985) ISBN 978-0823405640

12. *Town Mouse, Country Mouse,* by Jan Brett (Puffin, 2003) ISBN 978-0698119864

13. *The Wise Fool: Fables from the Islamic World,* by Shahrukh Husain and illustrated by Micha Archer (Barefoot Books, 2011) ISBN 978-1846862267

Stories

14. *Anansi and the Moss-Covered Rock,* retold by Eric A. Kimmel and illustrated by Janet Stevens (Holiday House, 1990) ISBN 978-0823407989

15. *Anansi the Spider: A Tale from the Ashanti,* by Gerald McDermott (Henry Holt, 1972) ISBN 978-0805003109

16. *Baby Rattlesnake: A Native American Tale,* by Te Ata and adapted by Lynn Moroney and illustrated by Mira Reisberg (Children's Book Press) ISBN 978-0892392162

17. *A Big Quiet House: A Yiddish Folktale from Eastern Europe,* retold by Heather Forest and illustrated by Susan Greenstein (August House Publishers, 2005) ISBN 978-0874834628

18. *The World of Winnie the Pooh and The House at Pooh Corner,* by A.A. Milne and illustrated by Ernest H. Shepard (Penguin, 2010) ISBN 978-0525444473

19. *How Chipmunk Got His Stripes,* by Joseph Bruchac & James Bruchac and illustrated by Jose Aruego and Ariane Dewey (Puffin, 2003) 978-0142500217

20. *It Could Always Be Worse: A Yiddish Folk Tale,* by Margot Zemach (Square Fish, 1990) ISBN 978-0374436360

21. *Medio Pollito/Half Chick: A Spanish Tale,* adapted by Eric A. Kimmel and illustrated by Valeria Docampo (Amazon Children's Publishing, 2010) ISBN 978-0761457053

22. *Nelson Mandela's Favorite African Folktales,* by Nelson Mandela (Norton, W. W. & Company, 2007) ISBN 978-0393329902

23. *One Grain of Rice: A Mathematical Folktale,* by Demi (Scholastic, 1997) ISBN 978-0590939980

24. *The People Could Fly: American Black Folktales,* retold by Virginia Hamilton and illustrated by Leo Dillon and Diane Dillon (Random House Children's Books, 1993) ISBN 978-0394869254

25. *A Story, A Story: An African Tale,* by Gail E. Haley (Aladdin, 1998) 978-0689712012

26. *The Tale of Peter Rabbit,* by Beatrix Potter and illustrated by Michael Hague (Chronicle Books, 2005) ISBN 978-0811849067

27. *Too Much Noise,* by Ann McGovern and illustrated by Simms Taback (Houghton Mifflin Harcourt, 1992) ISBN 978-0395629857

28. *The Tortoise's Gift: A Story from Zambia,* by Lari Don and illustrated by Melanie Williams (Barefoot Books, 2012) ISBN 978-1846867743

29. *Tunjur! Tunjur! Tunjur!: A Palestinian Folktale,* retold by Margaret Read MacDonald and illustrated by Alik Arzoumanian (Amazon Children's Publishing, 2012) ISBN 978-0761463122

Websites and Other Resources

Student Resources

1. Find the Main Idea Game
   http://bit.ly/XysFO4

2. Interactive Cinderella Story
   http://bit.ly/Qt3Yjb

3. Peter Rabbit World
   www.peterrabbit.com/en

Family Resources

4. Fables and Morals
   http://bit.ly/TeBs3d

5. Types of Fiction Characters
   http://bit.ly/XysYZr

Audio Versions

6. *Hear a Story: Medio Pollito,* by Eric Kimmel
   http://erickimmel.com/hear-a-story

Name _____

Directions: Think about what you heard in the read-aloud, and then fill in the chart using words or sentences.

Somebody	
Wanted	
But	
So	
Then	

Name _____

Directions: Use this story map to describe the characters, setting, and plot of the fable.

Title

Character(s)

Setting(s)

Plot

Beginning

Middle

End

Name _____

Directions: These three pictures show the beginning, middle, and end of "The Fox and the Grapes." Cut out the three pictures. Think about what is happening in each one. Put the pictures in order to show the beginning, middle, and end of the fable. Glue or tape them in the correct order on a piece of paper.

Name _____

Directions: Write the number that the teacher says beside the picture of the fable that is being described.

_____

_____

_____

_____

_____

_____

Dear Family Member,

We have finished the fables section of the Fables and Stories domain and are now listening to and discussing longer fictional stories. Today your child heard "The Little Half-Chick (Medio Pollito)," a Hispanic folktale. Over the next several days, s/he will also become familiar with "The Crowded, Noisy House," "The Tale of Peter Rabbit," and "All Stories are Anansi's."

Below are some suggestions for activities that you may do at home to continue enjoying the stories heard at school.

1. Storytelling Time

Have your child orally retell the story that s/he heard at school each day.

2. Character, Setting, and Plot

Talk with your child about the characters, setting, and plot of the stories. Ask questions about the story such as, "How did Peter Rabbit get into mischief?" Also, make personal connections to the stories with questions such as, "Have you ever gotten into mischief?"

3. Illustrating Stories

Have your child draw or paint a picture of one of the stories and then tell you about it. Again, ask questions to keep your child talking about the story. Another option is to create a three-part picture that shows the beginning, middle, and end of the story.

4. Sayings and Phrases: Do Unto Others as You Would Have Them Do Unto You

Your child has talked about this saying and its meaning at school. Talk with your child again about the meaning and ways to follow this saying. Find opportunities to compliment your child for following the Golden Rule.

5. Read Aloud Each Day

It is very important that you read to your child every day. The local library has folktales and collections of folktales that you can share with your child. Refer to the list of books and other relevant resources that was sent home with the previous family letter.

Be sure to talk about the characters, setting, and plot of these stories. You may also want to reread one that has been read at school.

Remember to let your child know how much you enjoy hearing about what s/he has learned at school.

Name _____

Directions: These pictures show some important parts of the plot of "The Tale of Peter Rabbit." Look at each picture and think about what is happening. Cut out the pictures and put them in order to show the correct sequence of events. Retell the story using the pictures. When you are sure that you have them in the correct order, glue or tape them on a separate sheet of paper in the correct order.

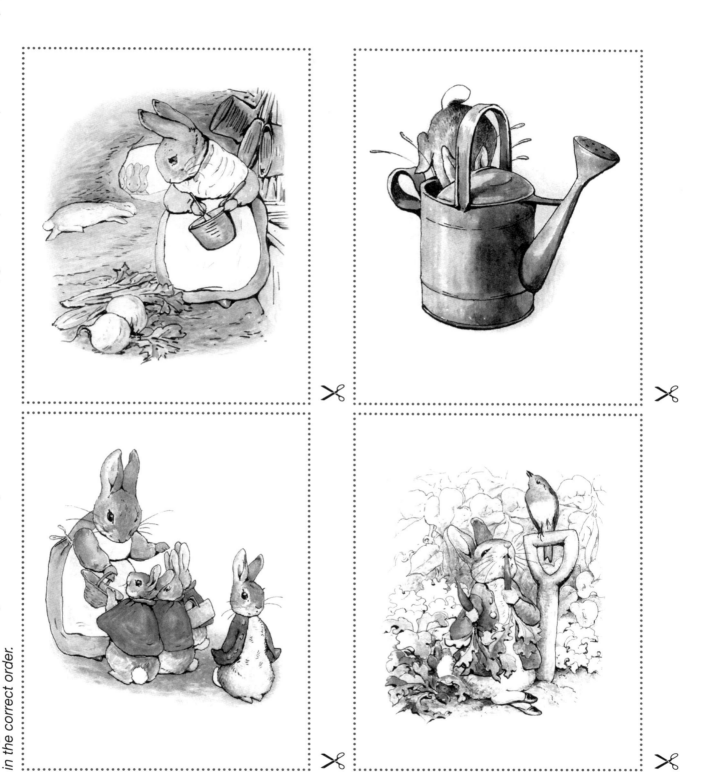

Directions: Listen to the sentence read by the teacher about fables and stories. Circle the smiling face if the sentence is true. Circle the frowning face if the sentence is false.

1. ☺   ☹

2. ☺   ☹

3. ☺   ☹

4. ☺   ☹

5. ☺   ☹

6. ☺   ☹

7. ☺   ☹

8. ☺   ☹

9. ☺   ☹

10. ☺   ☹

11.

12.

13.

Name _____

Directions: Listen to the sentence read by the teacher about fables and stories. Circle the smiling face if the sentence is true. Circle the frowning face if the sentence is false.

1. 🙂 ☹️

2. 🙂 ☹️

3. 🙂 ☹️

4. 🙂 ☹️

5. 🙂 ☹️

6. 🙂 ☹️

7. 🙂 ☹️

8. 🙂 ☹️

CORE KNOWLEDGE LANGUAGE ARTS

SERIES EDITOR-IN-CHIEF
E. D. Hirsch, Jr.

PRESIDENT
Linda Bevilacqua

EDITORIAL STAFF
Carolyn Gosse, Senior Editor - Preschool
Khara Turnbull, Materials Development Manager
Michelle L. Warner, Senior Editor - Listening & Learning

Mick Anderson
Robin Blackshire
Maggie Buchanan
Paula Coyner
Sue Fulton
Sara Hunt
Erin Kist
Robin Luecke
Rosie McCormick
Cynthia Peng
Liz Pettit
Ellen Sadler
Deborah Samley
Diane Auger Smith
Sarah Zelinke

DESIGN AND GRAPHICS STAFF
Scott Ritchie, Creative Director

Kim Berrall
Michael Donegan
Liza Greene
Matt Leech
Bridget Moriarty
Lauren Pack

CONSULTING PROJECT MANAGEMENT SERVICES
ScribeConcepts.com

ADDITIONAL CONSULTING SERVICES
Ang Blanchette
Dorrit Green
Carolyn Pinkerton

ACKNOWLEDGMENTS

These materials are the result of the work, advice, and encouragement of numerous individuals over many years. Some of those singled out here already know the depth of our gratitude; others may be surprised to find themselves thanked publicly for help they gave quietly and generously for the sake of the enterprise alone. To helpers named and unnamed we are deeply grateful.

CONTRIBUTORS TO EARLIER VERSIONS OF THESE MATERIALS
Susan B. Albaugh, Kazuko Ashizawa, Nancy Braier, Kathryn M. Cummings, Michelle De Groot, Diana Espinal, Mary E. Forbes, Michael L. Ford, Ted Hirsch, Danielle Knecht, James K. Lee, Diane Henry Leipzig, Martha G. Mack, Liana Mahoney, Isabel McLean, Steve Morrison, Juliane K. Munson, Elizabeth B. Rasmussen, Laura Tortorelli, Rachael L. Shaw, Sivan B. Sherman, Miriam E. Vidaver, Catherine S. Whittington, Jeannette A. Williams

We would like to extend special recognition to Program Directors Matthew Davis and Souzanne Wright who were instrumental to the early development of this program.

SCHOOLS
We are truly grateful to the teachers, students, and administrators of the following schools for their willingness to field test these materials and for their invaluable advice: Capitol View Elementary, Challenge Foundation Academy (IN), Community Academy Public Charter School, Lake Lure Classical Academy, Lepanto Elementary School, New Holland Core Knowledge Academy, Paramount School of Excellence, Pioneer Challenge Foundation Academy, New York City PS 26R (The Carteret School), PS 30X (Wilton School), PS 50X (Clara Barton School), PS 96Q, PS 102X (Joseph O. Loretan), PS 104Q (The Bays Water), PS 214K (Michael Friedsam), PS 223Q (Lyndon B. Johnson School), PS 308K (Clara Cardwell), PS 333Q (Goldie Maple Academy), Sequoyah Elementary School, South Shore Charter Public School, Spartanburg Charter School, Steed Elementary School, Thomas Jefferson Classical Academy, Three Oaks Elementary, West Manor Elementary.

And a special thanks to the CKLA Pilot Coordinators Anita Henderson, Yasmin Lugo-Hernandez, and Susan Smith, whose suggestions and day-to-day support to teachers using these materials in their classrooms was critical.

CREDITS

WRITERS
Matt Davis, Beatrix Potter

ILLUSTRATORS AND IMAGE SOURCES
Take Home Icon: Core Knowledge Staff; 6B-1: Core Knowledge Staff; 6B-2: Katy Cummings; PP-1a: Katy Cummings; PP-1b: Mary Parker; PP-1c: Mary Parker; PP-1d: Katy Cummings; PP-1e: Alycia Worthington; PP-1f: David Habben; PP-1a Answer Key: Katy Cummings; PP-1b Answer Key: Mary Parker; PP-1c Answer Key: Mary Parker; PP-1d Answer Key: Katy Cummings; PP-1e Answer Key: Alycia Worthington; PP-1f Answer Key: David Habben; 9B-1: Beatrix Potter

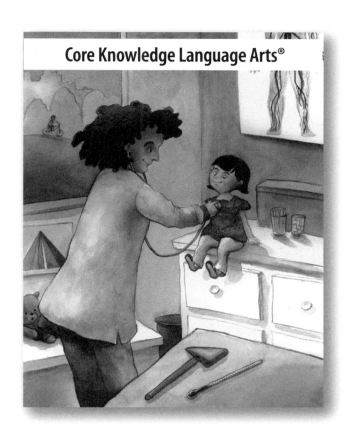

Domain 2: The Human Body

Tell it Again!™ Workbook

Listening & Learning™ Strand
GRADE 1

Amplify learning.

Core Knowledge®

Dear Family Member,

During the next several days, your child will be learning about the human body. S/he will learn about five important body systems: skeletal, muscular, digestive, circulatory, and nervous. Below are some suggestions of activities to do at home to reinforce what your child is learning about how our bodies work to keep us alive.

1. What's Inside My Body?

Ask your child to describe a body organ that s/he learns about each day. Have her/him tell you why the organ is important and the name of the body system to which it belongs.

2. Systems at Work

Ask your child which body systems are at work as you walk, talk, eat, and read together. Encourage the use of vocabulary being learned at school by asking your child to explain how the systems are working together.

3. Draw and Write

Have your child draw and/or write about what has been learned about each of the body systems and then share the drawing and/or writing with you. Ask questions to keep your child using the vocabulary learned at school.

4. Words to Use

Below are several of the words that your child will be learning about and using. Try to use these words as they come up in everyday speech with your child.

- *systems* — Human body systems include the digestive system and the circulatory system.
- *support* — The beams of the house support the roof.
- *voluntary* — His participation in the race was voluntary.
- *digestion* — The digestion of food takes the body several days to complete.
- *heart* — The heart is an involuntary muscle.
- *nerves* — The tips of your fingers are full of nerves that allow you to feel.

5. Read Aloud Each Day

It is very important to read with your child each day. Please refer to the list sent home with this family letter of recommended trade books related to the human body that may be found at the library, as well as informative websites.

Be sure to praise your child whenever s/he shares what has been learned at school.

Recommended Resources for The Human Body

Trade Books

1. *The Busy Body Book,* by Lizzy Rockwell (Random House Children's Books, 2008) ISBN 978-0553113747

2. *The Circulatory System (Human Body Systems),* by Helen Frost (Capstone Press, 2006) ISBN 978-0736887762

3. *The Digestive System (Human Body Systems),* by Helen Frost (Capstone Press, 2000) ISBN 978-0736806497

4. *Eat Healthy, Feel Great,* by William Sears, M.D., Martha Sears, R.N., and Christie Watts Kelly, illustrated by Renee Andriani (Little, Brown and Company, 2002) ISBN 978-0316787086

5. *Eating Well (Looking After Me),* by Liz Gogerly and Mike Gordon (Crabtree Publishing Company, 2009) ISBN 978-0778741176

6. *First Encyclopedia of the Human Body (DK First Reference Series),* edited by Penny Smith (DK Children, 2005) ISBN 978-0756609979

7. *Germs Make Me Sick!,* by Melvin Berger, illustrated by Marylin Hafner (Scott Foresman, 1995) ISBN 978-0064451543

8. *Healthy Eating (Science Everywhere!),* by Helen Orme (New Forest Press, 2010) ISBN 978-1848982895

9. *Hear Your Heart (Let's-Read-and-Find-Out Science: Stage 1,* by Paul Showers, illustrated by Holly Keller (Perfection Learning, 2001) ISBN 978-0812458206

10. *How Does Your Brain Work (Rookie Read-About Health),* by Don L. Curry (Children's Press, 2004) ISBN 978-0516278537

11. *How to Stay Healthy (I Know That!),* by Claire Llewellyn (Sea-to-Sea Publishing, 2007) ISBN 978-1597710244

12. *It's Catching: Colds,* by Angela Royston (Heinemann, 2001) ISBN 978-1588102270

13. *Louis Pasteur,* by Kremena Spengler (Capstone Press, 2003) ISBN 978-0736834414

14. *The Magic School Bus Inside the Human Body,* by Joanna Cole and Bruce Degen (Scholastic Press, 1990) ISBN 978-0590414272

15. *Me and My Amazing Body,* written and illustrated by Joan Sweeney (Dragonfly Books, 2000) ISBN 978-0375806230

16. *The Muscular System (Human Body Systems),* by Helen Frost (Capstone Press, 2000) ISBN 978-0736806503

17. *My Body (Science Books S),* by Patty Carratello (Teacher Created Resources, 2004) ISBN 978-1557342119

18. *My First Visit to the Doctor,* by Eve Marleau and Michael Garton (QEB Publishing, 2009) ISBN 978-1595669872

19. *My Healthy Body,* by Bobbie Kalman (Crabtree Publishing Company, 2010) ISBN 978-0778794714

20. *The Nervous System (Human Body Systems),* by Helen Frost (Capstone Press, 2000) ISBN 978-0736806510

21. *Oh, the Things You Can Do That Are Good For You!,* by Tish Rabe and illustrated by Aristides Ruiz (Random House, Inc., 2001) ISBN 978-0375810985

22. *The Skeletal System (Human Body Systems),* by Helen Frost (Capstone Press, 2000). ISBN 978-0736806534

23. *Stay Fit (Snap Books: Healthy Me),* by Sara R. Hunt (Capstone Press, 2011) ISBN 978-1429672931

24. *Think, Think, Think: Learning About Your Brain (Amazing Body),* by Hill Nettleton (Picture Window Books, 2006) ISBN 978-1404805033

25. *What Happens to a Hamburger? (Let's-Read-and-Find-Out Science, Stage 2),* by Paul Showers and illustrated by Edward Miller (Harper Collins, 2001) ISBN 978-0064451833

Websites and Other Resources

Student Resources

1. Children's Museum of New York
    http://www.cmom.org/explore/exhibits/
    eat_sleep_play_building_health_every_day

2. Digestive System Video
    http://kidshealth.org/kid/htbw/_bfs_DSmoviesource.html

3. Food Plate "Blast Off Game"
    http://www.fns.usda.gov/multimedia/Games/Blastoff/BlastOff_Game.html

4. Kids' Biology
    http://www.kidsbiology.com/human_biology/index.php

5. "A Kid's Guide to Shots"
    http://kidshealth.org/kid/stay_healthy/body/guide_shots.html

6. Kids' Health Skeletal System Video
    http://kidshealth.org/kid/htbw/_bfs_SSmoviesource.html

7. Muscular System Video
    http://www.makemegenius.com/video_play.php?id=100

8. Nervous System Video
    http://kidshealth.org/kid/htbw/_bfs_NSmoviesource.html

Family Resources

9. Circulatory System Video
    http://www.neok12.com/php/watch.php?v=zX760b6c717d557e72515
    c02&t=Circulatory-System

10. Heart and Healthy Living
    http://www.mplsheartfoundation.org/kids/lets_learn.html

11. The Human Brain
    http://www.learner.org/series/discoveringpsychology/brain/brain_flash.html

Name _____

My _____ System

Directions: Complete the title line with the name of the system being reviewed. Next, draw the organs included in that system within the body form. Use the lines at the bottom of the page to write a sentence about the system.

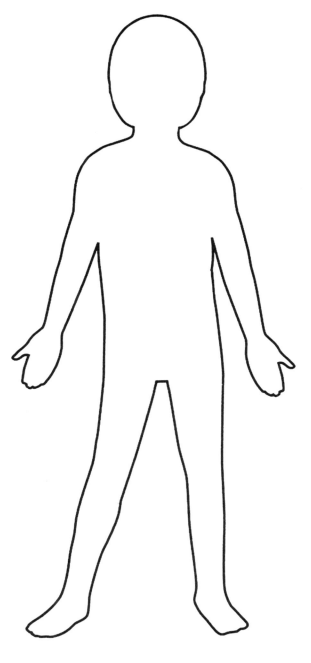

_____

_____

Dear Family Member,

I hope your child has enjoyed learning about her/his body and how its systems work together to keep us alive. Over the next several days, s/he will learn about health and nutrition—ways to keep her/his body at its best. Below are some suggestions for activities that you may do at home to reinforce the healthy habits s/he is learning about at school.

1. Food Pyramid Fun

Visit the USDA website to learn more about a healthy diet: www.choosemyplate.gov. Play one of the learning games with your child, asking questions to encourage the use of vocabulary learned at school.

2. Menu Planning, Shopping, and Cooking

Have your child help you plan a well-balanced meal—using foods from a variety of food groups—for the family's dinner. Then, go to the grocery store together to buy the ingredients. Have him/her help in the preparation of the food.

3. Words to Use

Below are several of the words that your child will be learning about and using. Try to use these words as they come up in everyday speech with your child.

- *diseases*—Scientists work hard to cure diseases that make people sick.

- *nutritious*—Every day, Luke ate a nutritious lunch with fruits and vegetables.

- *balanced diet*—Jeannette's father made sure she had a balanced diet by serving a variety of foods throughout the day.

- *complicated*—The recipe was extremely complicated and had many steps to follow.

4. Read Aloud Each Day

It is important to read to your child each day. Please refer to the list sent home with the previous family letter of recommended trade books related to the human body that may be found at the library. That list also contains informative websites.

6. Sayings and Phrases: An Apple a Day Keeps the Doctor Away

Your child will learn the saying: "An apple a day keeps the doctor away." Talk with your child about its meaning. Discuss the importance of going to the doctor for regular checkups and vaccinations.

Be sure to praise your child whenever s/he shares what has been learned at school.

Name _____

Body Systems

Directions: Identify pictures of the nervous, digestive, circulatory, and muscular systems. Write the number on the line next to its corresponding picture.

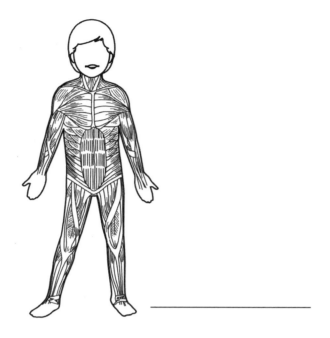

_____

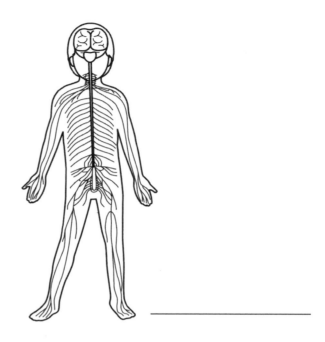

_____

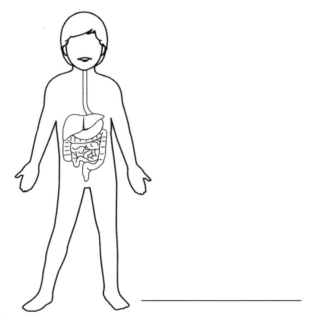

_____

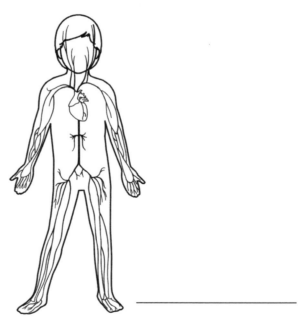

_____

1. Nervous system   2. Digestive system

3. Circulatory system   4. Muscular system

Directions: Think about what you heard in the read-aloud, and then fill in the chart using words or sentences.

Somebody	
Wanted	
But	
So	
Then	

Name _____

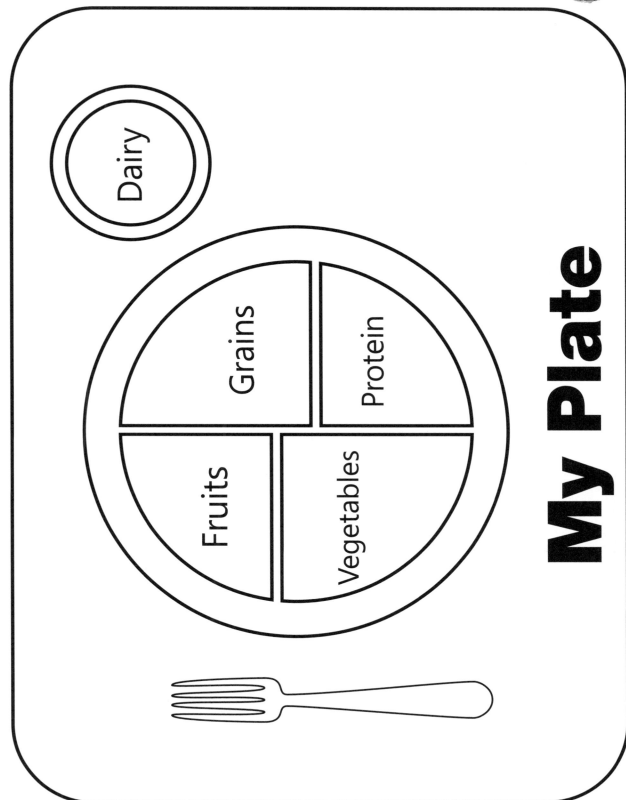

My Plate

Dairy

Grains

Protein

Fruits

Vegetables

Directions: Color the "vegetable" section green; the "fruit" section red; the "grains" section orange; the "protein" section purple; and the "dairy" section blue.

Name _____

Directions: Cut out the pictures. Follow the teacher's instructions.

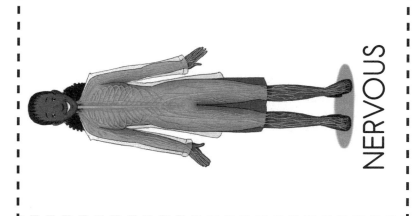

NERVOUS

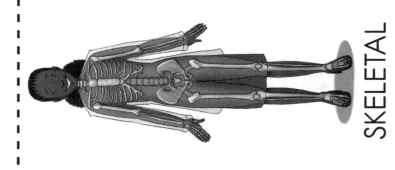

SKELETAL

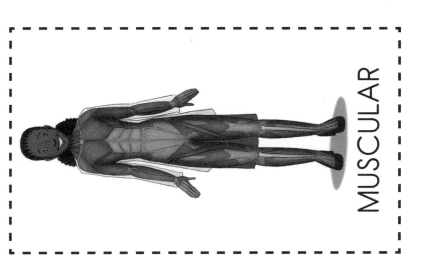

MUSCULAR

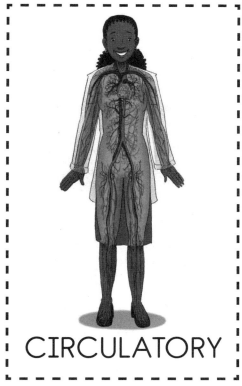

CIRCULATORY

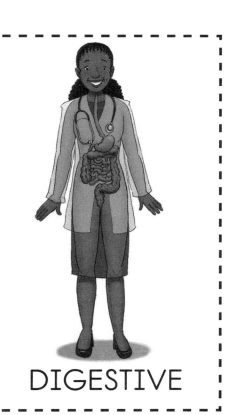

DIGESTIVE

Name _____

Directions: Listen to your teacher's instructions.

1.

2.

3.

4.

5.

6.

7.

8.

9.

10.

11. 🙂 ☹️

12. 🙂 ☹️

13. 🙂 ☹️

14. 🙂 ☹️

15. 🙂 ☹️

Name _____

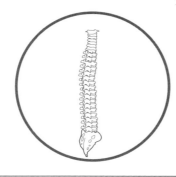

Directions: Listen to the teacher's instructions. Then, draw a circle around the correct picture(s) in each row.

1.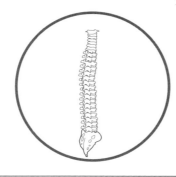

2.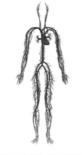

3.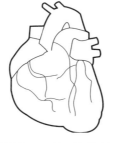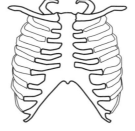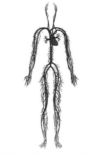

4.

5.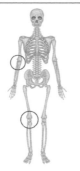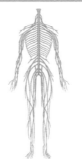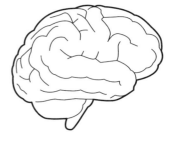

The Human Body **21**

6.

7.

8.

9.

10.

Name _____

A Well-Balanced Meal (Grains, Fruits, Vegetables, Meat and Beans, Milk)

Directions: Create a healthy meal to fill the empty plate. Include foods from all food groups.

Name _____

Five Keys to Keeping Healthy

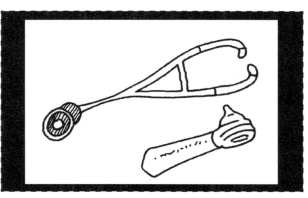

Directions: Identify and discuss what each picture shows. Cut out the pictures and glue or tape each one under the correct heading on CA-1.

Name _____

Five Keys to Keeping Healthy

🔑 Eat Well	🔑 Exercise
🔑 Keep Clean	🔑 Rest
🔑 Have Checkups	

CORE KNOWLEDGE LANGUAGE ARTS

SERIES EDITOR-IN-CHIEF
E. D. Hirsch, Jr.

PRESIDENT
Linda Bevilacqua

EDITORIAL STAFF
Carolyn Gosse, Senior Editor - Preschool
Khara Turnbull, Materials Development Manager
Michelle L. Warner, Senior Editor - Listening & Learning

Mick Anderson
Robin Blackshire
Maggie Buchanan
Paula Coyner
Sue Fulton
Sara Hunt
Erin Kist
Robin Luecke
Rosie McCormick
Cynthia Peng
Liz Pettit
Ellen Sadler
Deborah Samley
Diane Auger Smith
Sarah Zelinke

DESIGN AND GRAPHICS STAFF
Scott Ritchie, Creative Director

Kim Berrall
Michael Donegan
Liza Greene
Matt Leech
Bridget Moriarty
Lauren Pack

CONSULTING PROJECT MANAGEMENT SERVICES
ScribeConcepts.com

ADDITIONAL CONSULTING SERVICES
Ang Blanchette
Dorrit Green
Carolyn Pinkerton

ACKNOWLEDGMENTS

These materials are the result of the work, advice, and encouragement of numerous individuals over many years. Some of those singled out here already know the depth of our gratitude; others may be surprised to find themselves thanked publicly for help they gave quietly and generously for the sake of the enterprise alone. To helpers named and unnamed we are deeply grateful.

CONTRIBUTORS TO EARLIER VERSIONS OF THESE MATERIALS
Susan B. Albaugh, Kazuko Ashizawa, Nancy Braier, Kathryn M. Cummings, Michelle De Groot, Diana Espinal, Mary E. Forbes, Michael L. Ford, Ted Hirsch, Danielle Knecht, James K. Lee, Diane Henry Leipzig, Martha G. Mack, Liana Mahoney, Isabel McLean, Steve Morrison, Juliane K. Munson, Elizabeth B. Rasmussen, Laura Tortorelli, Rachael L. Shaw, Sivan B. Sherman, Miriam E. Vidaver, Catherine S. Whittington, Jeannette A. Williams

We would like to extend special recognition to Program Directors Matthew Davis and Souzanne Wright who were instrumental to the early development of this program.

SCHOOLS
We are truly grateful to the teachers, students, and administrators of the following schools for their willingness to field test these materials and for their invaluable advice: Capitol View Elementary, Challenge Foundation Academy (IN), Community Academy Public Charter School, Lake Lure Classical Academy, Lepanto Elementary School, New Holland Core Knowledge Academy, Paramount School of Excellence, Pioneer Challenge Foundation Academy, New York City PS 26R (The Carteret School), PS 30X (Wilton School), PS 50X (Clara Barton School), PS 96Q, PS 102X (Joseph O. Loretan), PS 104Q (The Bays Water), PS 214K (Michael Friedsam), PS 223Q (Lyndon B. Johnson School), PS 308K (Clara Cardwell), PS 333Q (Goldie Maple Academy), Sequoyah Elementary School, South Shore Charter Public School, Spartanburg Charter School, Steed Elementary School, Thomas Jefferson Classical Academy, Three Oaks Elementary, West Manor Elementary.

And a special thanks to the CKLA Pilot Coordinators Anita Henderson, Yasmin Lugo-Hernandez, and Susan Smith, whose suggestions and day-to-day support to teachers using these materials in their classrooms was critical.

CREDITS

EXPERT REVIEWER

Craig Hanke

WRITERS

Beth Engel

ILLUSTRATORS AND IMAGE SOURCES

Take-Home Icon: Core Knowledge Staff; 9B-1: Core Knowledge Staff; 10B-1: Apryl Scott; DA-2: Shutterstock; DA-2 Answer Key: Shutterstock; DA-3: Shutterstock

Domain 3:
Different Lands, Similar Stories

Tell it Again!™ Workbook

Listening & Learning™ Strand

GRADE 1

Amplify learning.

Core Knowledge®

Name _____

Directions: Think about what you heard in the read-aloud, and then fill in the chart using words or sentences.

Somebody	
Wanted	
But	
So	
Then	

Dear Family Member,

Today your child listened to "Cinderella," a fairy tale that originated in France. Over the next few days, your child will hear fairy tales with similar themes that originated in Egypt and Ireland. Similarly, your child will hear folktales from around the world that feature people who are no bigger than the size of a thumb: "Tom Thumb," from England; "Thumbelina," from Denmark; and "Issun Boshi," from Japan.

Below are some suggestions for activities that you may do at home to continue enjoying the folktales heard at school and to reinforce the idea that different countries or lands tell similar stories.

1. "Cinderella"

Reread "Cinderella" with your child to increase your child's awareness of the similarities and differences between this fairy tale and the stories that originated in Egypt and Ireland. Although your child will hear several fairy tales that share themes with "Cinderella," there are many other variations in print. Tell or read to your child different versions of the folktale. Talk about how the different versions are the same and how they are different.

2. Character, Setting, Plot, Conflict

Talk with your child about the characters, setting, plot, and conflict (or problem) of the folktales and fairy tales. Ask questions about the tales such as, "Who became royalty in the end?"

3. Storytelling Time

Have your child orally retell the story that s/he heard at school each day, pointing out on a world map or globe where the folktale originated. Today's fairy tale originated in France. The fairy tales in the next lessons originated in Egypt and Ireland.

4. Sayings and Phrases: There's No Place Like Home

Your child will talk about this saying and its meaning at school in relation to "Tom Thumb." Talk with your child again about the meaning and situations in which you can use this saying and how this saying relates to the folktale "Tom Thumb."

5. Read Aloud Each Day

Set aside time to read to your child every day. Please refer to the list of books and other resources sent home with this family letter, recommending resources related to this domain. Be sure to talk about the characters, setting, and plot of these stories. You may also want to reread one that has been read at school.

Be sure to let your child know how much you enjoy hearing about what s/he has been learning at school.

Recommended Resources for Different Lands, Similar Stories

Trade Book List

Rags-to-Riches Folktales

1. *Cendrillon: A Caribbean Cinderella,* by Robert D. San Souci and illustrated by Brian Pinkney (Aladdin, 2002) ISBN 978-0689848889

2. *Domitilla: A Cinderella Tale from the Mexican Tradition,* adapted by Jewell Reinhart Coburn and illustrated by Connie McLennan (Shen's Books, 2000) ISBN 978-1885008138

3. *The Egyptian Cinderella,* by Shirley Climo and illustrated by Ruth Heller (HarperCollins, 1992) ISBN 978-0064432795

4. *The Gift of the Crocodile: A Cinderella Story,* by Judy Sierra and illustrated by Reynold Ruffins (Simon & Schuster Books for Young Readers) ISBN 978-0689821882

5. *The Golden Sandal: A Middle Eastern Cinderella Story,* by Rebecca Hickox and illustrated by Will Hillenbrand (Holiday House, 1999) ISBN 978-0823415137

6. *The Irish Cinderlad,* by Shirley Climo and illustrated by Loretta Krupinski (Turtleback, 2000) ISBN 978-0613285407

7. *The Korean Cinderella,* by Shirley Climo and illustrated by Ruth Heller (HarperCollins, 1996) ISBN 978-0064433976

8. *Little Gold Star: A Spanish American Cinderella Tale,* by Robert D. San Souci and illustrated by Sergio Martinez (HarperCollins, 2000) ISBN 978-0688147808

9. *Mufaro's Beautiful Daughters,* by John Steptoe (Lothrop, Lee and Shepard Books,1987) ISBN 978-0688040451

10. *Princess Furball,* by Charlotte Huck and Anita Lobel (Greenwillow Books, 1994) ISBN 978-0688131074

11. *Yeh-Shen: A Cinderella Story from China,* retold by Ai-Ling Louie and illustrated by Ed Young (Puffin, 1996) ISBN 978-0698113886

Thumb-Sized People Folktales

12. *Issun Boshi: One-Inch Boy: A Japanese Folktale (Folktales from Around the World),* retold by Nadia Higgins and illustrated by J.T. Morrow (Child's World, 2011) ISBN 978-1609731397

13. *Thumbelina,* by Brad Sneed (Dial, 2004) ISBN 978-0803728127

14. *Tom Thumb,* illustrated by Claudia Venturini (Child's Play International, 2008) ISBN 978-1846431166

Cunning Animal Folktales

15. *Little Red Riding Hood,* by Jerry Pinkney (Little, Brown Books for Young Readers, 2007) ISBN 978-0316013550

16. *Lon Po Po: A Red-Riding Hood Story from China,* by Ed Young (Puffin, 1996) ISBN 978-0698113824

17. *Pretty Salma: A Little Red Riding Hood Story from Africa,* by Niki Daly (Clarion Books, 2007) ISBN 978-0618723454

18. *Red Riding Hood,* retold and illustrated by James Marshall (Picture Puffins, 1993) ISBN 978-0140546934

Different Lands Nonfiction

19. *Botswana in Pictures (Visual Geography),* by Alison Behnke (Twentyfirst Century Books, 2009) ISBN 978-1575059532

20. *China (Countries of the World),* by Michael Dahl (Capstone, 1999) ISBN 978-0736880596

21. *Denmark (Countries of the World),* by Patricia J. Murphy (Capstone, 2002) ISBN 978-0736813716

22. *England (Countries of the World),* by Kathleen W. Deady (Capstone, 2006) ISBN 978-0736847346

23. *Getting to Know France and French,* by Nicola Wright and illustrated by Kim Wooley (Barron's Educational Series, 1993) ISBN 978-0812015324

24. *Ireland (A to Z),* by Justine Fontes and Ron Fontes (Children's Press, 2004) ISBN 978-0516268101

25. *Japan (Countries of the World),* by Michael Dahl (Capstone, 1999) ISBN 978-0736880589

26. *Look What Came from Egypt,* by Miles Harvey (Children's Press, 1999) ISBN 978-0531159378

27. *Look What Came from Germany,* by Kevin Davis (Franklin Watts, 2000) ISBN 978-0531164358

Websites and Other Resources

Student Resources

1. Cinderella Read-Aloud
   http://www.learner.org/interactives/story/Cinderella.html

2. Elements of Stories
   http://www.flocabulary.com/fivethings

Directions: Think about how "Cinderella," "The Girl with the Red Slippers," and "Billy Beg" are similar and how they are different. Label each circle for each story. Draw or write how they are alike in the overlapping part of the circles. Draw or write how the stories are different in the parts of the circles that do not overlap.

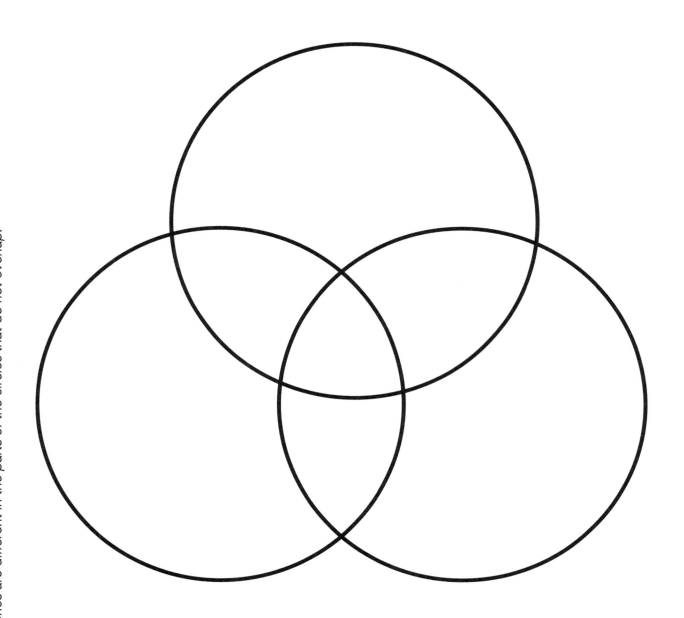

Different Lands, Similar Stories

Name _____

Directions: Listen to the teacher's instructions. Next, look at the two pictures in the row and find the one that answers the question. Circle the correct picture.

1.

2.

3.

4.

5.

6.

Name _____

Directions: Cut out the four pictures. Arrange the pictures in order to show the proper sequence of events. Once they have been sequenced, glue or tape the pictures on a piece of paper.

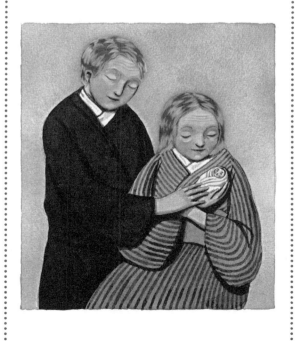

7B-1

Dear Family Member,

Today your child listened to the folktale "Little Red Riding Hood," which originated in Germany. Over the next several days, your child will hear two more folktales that are similar to "Little Red Riding Hood": "Hu Gu Po" from China, and "Tselane" from Botswana.

Below are some suggestions for activities that you may do at home to continue enjoying the folktales heard at school, and to reinforce the idea that different countries or lands tell similar stories.

1. Character, Setting, Plot, Conflict

Talk with your child about the characters, setting, plot, and conflict (or problem) of the folktales. Ask questions about the tales such as, "Why did Little Red Riding Hood have to walk through the woods? Where was she going?" Also, make personal connections to the folktales such as, "What should you do if you're approached by a stranger?"

2. Different Versions of Folktales

Although your child will hear a few folktales whose characters have similar adventures, there are many other variations in print. Tell or read to your child different versions of these folktales and talk about how the different versions are the same or different.

3. Storytelling Time

Have your child orally retell the story that s/he hears at school each day, pointing out on a world map or globe where the folktale originated. Countries will be introduced in the following order: Germany, China, and Botswana.

4. Read Aloud Each Day

Set aside time to read to your child every day. Please refer to the list of books and other resources sent home with the previous family letter, recommending resources related to this domain. Be sure to talk about the characters, setting, and plot of these stories. You may also want to reread one that has been read at school.

Be sure to let your child know how much you enjoy hearing about what s/he has been learning at school.

Name _____

Directions: Think about how "Little Red Riding Hood," "Hu Gu Po," and "Tselane" are similar and how they are different. Label each circle for each story. Draw or write how they are alike in the overlapping part of the circles. Draw or write how the stories are different in the parts of the circles that do not overlap.

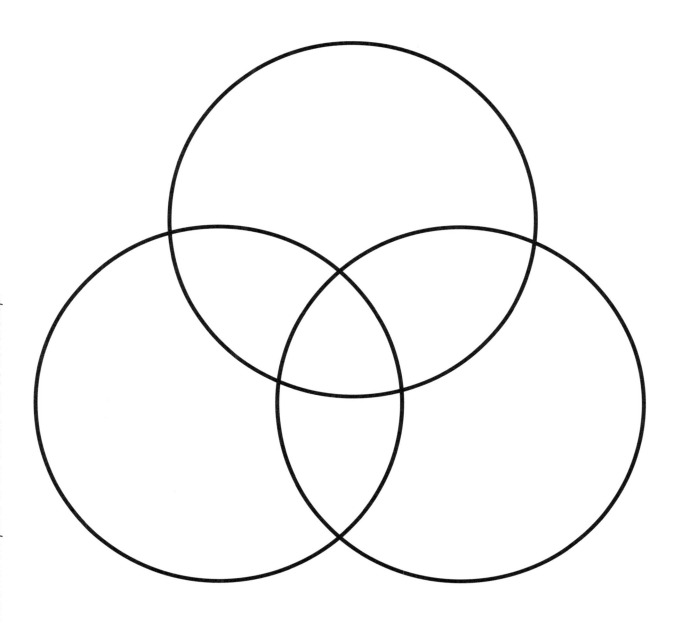

Name _____

Directions: Listen carefully to the words and sentences read by your teacher. If the sentence uses the word correctly, circle the smiling face. If the sentence does not use the word correctly, circle the frowning face.

1.

2.

3.

4.

5.

6.

7.

8.

9.

10.

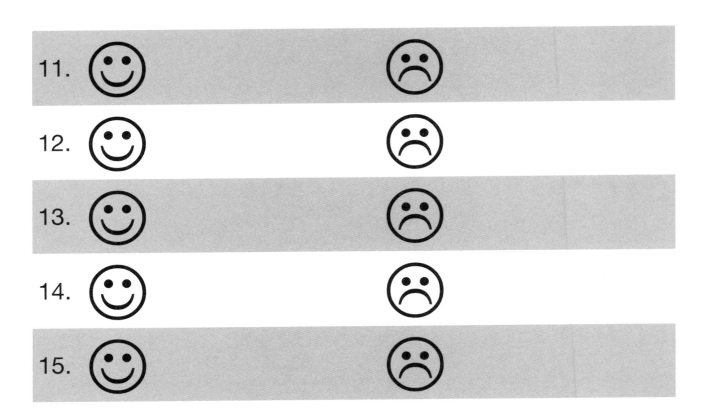

11.

12.

13.

14.

15.

Name _____

Directions: Listen to the sentence read by the teacher about folktales. Circle the smiling face if the sentence is correct. Circle the frowning face if the sentence is not correct.

1. 🙂 ☹️

2. 🙂 ☹️

3. 🙂 ☹️

4. 🙂 ☹️

5. 🙂 ☹️

6. 🙂 ☹️

7. 🙂 ☹️

8. 🙂 ☹️

9. 🙂 ☹️

10. 🙂 ☹️

CORE KNOWLEDGE LANGUAGE ARTS

SERIES EDITOR-IN-CHIEF
E. D. Hirsch, Jr.

PRESIDENT
Linda Bevilacqua

EDITORIAL STAFF
Carolyn Gosse, Senior Editor - Preschool
Khara Turnbull, Materials Development Manager
Michelle L. Warner, Senior Editor - Listening & Learning

Mick Anderson
Robin Blackshire
Maggie Buchanan
Paula Coyner
Sue Fulton
Sara Hunt
Erin Kist
Robin Luecke
Rosie McCormick
Cynthia Peng
Liz Pettit
Ellen Sadler
Deborah Samley
Diane Auger Smith
Sarah Zelinke

DESIGN AND GRAPHICS STAFF
Scott Ritchie, Creative Director

Kim Berrall
Michael Donegan
Liza Greene
Matt Leech
Bridget Moriarty
Lauren Pack

CONSULTING PROJECT MANAGEMENT SERVICES
ScribeConcepts.com

ADDITIONAL CONSULTING SERVICES
Ang Blanchette
Dorrit Green
Carolyn Pinkerton

ACKNOWLEDGMENTS

These materials are the result of the work, advice, and encouragement of numerous individuals over many years. Some of those singled out here already know the depth of our gratitude; others may be surprised to find themselves thanked publicly for help they gave quietly and generously for the sake of the enterprise alone. To helpers named and unnamed we are deeply grateful.

CONTRIBUTORS TO EARLIER VERSIONS OF THESE MATERIALS

Susan B. Albaugh, Kazuko Ashizawa, Nancy Braier, Kathryn M. Cummings, Michelle De Groot, Diana Espinal, Mary E. Forbes, Michael L. Ford, Ted Hirsch, Danielle Knecht, James K. Lee, Diane Henry Leipzig, Martha G. Mack, Liana Mahoney, Isabel McLean, Steve Morrison, Juliane K. Munson, Elizabeth B. Rasmussen, Laura Tortorelli, Rachael L. Shaw, Sivan B. Sherman, Miriam E. Vidaver, Catherine S. Whittington, Jeannette A. Williams

We would like to extend special recognition to Program Directors Matthew Davis and Souzanne Wright who were instrumental to the early development of this program.

SCHOOLS

We are truly grateful to the teachers, students, and administrators of the following schools for their willingness to field test these materials and for their invaluable advice: Capitol View Elementary, Challenge Foundation Academy (IN), Community Academy Public Charter School, Lake Lure Classical Academy, Lepanto Elementary School, New Holland Core Knowledge Academy, Paramount School of Excellence, Pioneer Challenge Foundation Academy, New York City PS 26R (The Carteret School), PS 30X (Wilton School), PS 50X (Clara Barton School), PS 96Q, PS 102X (Joseph O. Loretan), PS 104Q (The Bays Water), PS 214K (Michael Friedsam), PS 223Q (Lyndon B. Johnson School), PS 308K (Clara Cardwell), PS 333Q (Goldie Maple Academy), Sequoyah Elementary School, South Shore Charter Public School, Spartanburg Charter School, Steed Elementary School, Thomas Jefferson Classical Academy, Three Oaks Elementary, West Manor Elementary.

And a special thanks to the CKLA Pilot Coordinators Anita Henderson, Yasmin Lugo-Hernandez, and Susan Smith, whose suggestions and day-to-day support to teachers using these materials in their classrooms was critical.

CREDITS

Every effort has been taken to trace and acknowledge copyrights. The editors tender their apologies for any accidental infringement where copyright has proved untraceable. They would be pleased to insert the appropriate acknowledgment in any subsequent edition of this publication. Trademarks and trade names are shown in this publication for illustrative purposes only and are the property of their respective owners. The references to trademarks and trade names given herein do not affect their validity.

The Word Work exercises are based on the work of Beck, McKeown, and Kucan in Bringing Words to Life *(The Guilford Press, 2002).*

All photographs are used under license from Shutterstock, Inc. unless otherwise noted.

WRITERS
Matt Davis, Rosie McCormick

ILLUSTRATORS AND IMAGE SOURCES
Take Home Icon: Core Knowledge Staff; PP-1 (1a, 4b, 6a): Gideon Kendall; PP-1 (1b, 3a): Barry Gott; PP-1 (2a, 3b, 6b): Kimberli Johnson; PP-1 (2b): Gail McIntosh; PP-1 (4a, 5b): Shari Griffiths; PP-1 (5a): Kristin Kwan; PP-1 Answer Key (1a, 4b, 6a): Gideon Kendall; PP-1 Answer Key (1b, 3a): Barry Gott; PP-1 Answer Key (2a, 3b, 6b): Kimberli Johnson; PP-1 Answer Key (2b): Gail McIntosh; PP-1 Answer Key (4a, 5b): Shari Griffiths; PP-1 Answer Key (5a): Kristin Kwan; PP-2: Kristin Kwan; PP-2 Answer Key: Kristin Kwan

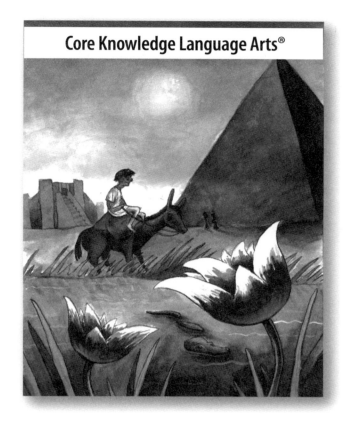

Domain 4:
Early World Civilizations

Tell it Again!™ Workbook

Listening & Learning™ Strand

GRADE 1

Amplify learning.

Core Knowledge®

Name _____

Dear Family Member,

During the next several days, your child will be learning about the ancient civilization of Mesopotamia. S/he will learn about the importance of the Tigris and Euphrates rivers for farming and for the cities that grew where people settled. Your child will also learn about the development of a system of writing called cuneiform, the existence of leaders called kings, and the importance of religion. Your child will come to understand that it is because of these key components that Mesopotamia is considered a civilization. Below are some suggestions for activities that you may do at home to reinforce what your child is learning about Mesopotamia.

1. Where Are We?

Have your child locate the area known as Mesopotamia (located in the Middle East) on a world map or globe. (If you do not have a map, check one out from the library.) Talk about the geography of this area. (desert, Tigris and Euphrates rivers, etc.)

2. Draw and Write

Have your child draw and/or write about what has been learned about Mesopotamia and then share the drawing with you. Ask questions to keep your child using the vocabulary learned at school.

3. Compare Civilizations

Compare/contrast the farming, cities, writing, leaders, and religion of Mesopotamia and the United States. Talk about the importance of each of these components in any civilization.

4. Read Aloud Each Day

It is very important that you read to your child each day. The local library has many books on Mesopotamia, and a list of books and other resources relevant to this topic is attached to this letter.

5. The Golden Rule

Your child will learn the Golden Rule: "Do unto others as you would have them do unto you." Talk with your child about the meaning of this saying and ways to follow it. Find opportunities to compliment your child for following the Golden Rule.

Be sure to let your child know how much you enjoy hearing about what s/he has been learning at school.

Recommended Trade Books for Early World Civilizations

Trade Book List

1. *Archaeologists Dig for Clues (Let's-Read-and-Find-Out-Science 2),* by Kate Duke (HarperTrophy, 1996) ISBN 978-0064451758

Mesopotamia

2. *Gilgamesh the King (The Gilgamesh Trilogy),* retold and illustrated by Ludmila Zeman (Tundra Books, 1998) ISBN 978-0887764370

3. *Mesopotamia,* edited by E.D. Hirsch, Jr. (Pearson Learning, 2002) ISBN 978-0769050041

Ancient Egypt

4. *Ancient Egypt (DK Eyewitness Books),* by George Hart (DK CHILDREN; Har/Cdr/Ch edition, 2008) ISBN 978-0756637651

5. *Ancient Egypt,* edited by E.D. Hirsch, Jr. (Pearson Learning, 2002) ISBN 978-0769050058

6. *Bill and Pete Go Down the Nile,* by Tomie DePaola (Puffin, 1996) ISBN 978-0698114012

7. *The Egyptian Cinderella,* by Shirley Climo (HarperCollins, 1992) ISBN 978-0064432795

8. *Egyptian Gods and Goddesses (All Aboard Reading),* by Henry Barker (Penguin Young Readers, 1999) ISBN 978-0448420295

9. *The 5000-Year-Old Puzzle: Solving a Mystery of Ancient Egypt,* by Claudia Logan (Farrar, Straus and Giroux, 2002) ISBN 978-0374323356

10. *Mummies and Pyramids (Magic Tree House Research Guide),* by Will Osborne and Mary Pope Osborne (Random House Books for Young Readers, 2001) ISBN 978-0375802980

11. *Mummies in the Morning (Magic Tree House #3),* by Mary Pope Osborne (Random House Books for Young Readers, 1993) ISBN 978-0679824244

12. *Mummies Made in Egypt,* by Aliki (HarperTrophy, 1985) ISBN 978-0064460118

13. *The Nile River (Rookie Read-About Geography),* by Allan Fowler (Children's Press, 2000) ISBN 978-0516265599

14. *The Pharaohs of Ancient Egypt (Landmark Books),* by Elizabeth Payne (Random House Books for Young Readers, 1981) ISBN 978-0394846996

15. *Season of the Sandstorms (Magic Tree House, No. 34),* by Mary Pope Osborne and Sal Murdocca (Random House Books for Young Readers, 2006) ISBN 978-0375830327

16. *Seeker of Knowledge: The Man Who Deciphered Egyptian Hieroglyphs,* by James Rumford (Houghton Mifflin, 2003) ISBN 978-0618333455

Three World Religions

17. *Celebrate Hanukkah with Light, Latkes and Dreidels,* by Deborah Heiligman (National Geographic, 2006) ISBN 978-0792259251

18. *Exodus,* by Brian Wildsmith (Eerdmans Books for Young Readers, 1998) ISBN 978-0802851758

19. *Golden Domes and Silver Lanterns: A Muslim Book of Colors,* by Hena Khan (Chronicle Books, 2012) ISBN 978-0811879057

20. *It's Seder Time!,* by Latifa Berry Kropf (Kar-Ben Publishing, 2004) ISBN 978-1580130929

21. *Jesus,* by Brian Wildsmith (Eerdmans Books for Young Readers, 2000) ISBN 978-0802852120

22. *Joseph,* by Brian Wildsmith (William B. Eerdmans Publishing Company, 1997) ISBN 978-0802851611

23. *The Miracles of Jesus,* illustrated by Tomie dePaola (Penguin Group, 2008) ISBN 978-0142410684

24. *My First Ramadan,* by Karen Katz (Henry Holt and Co., 2007) ISBN 978-0805078947

25. *My Muslim Faith,* by Khadijah Knight (Cherrytree Books, 2006) ISBN 978-1842343913

26. *One World, Many Religions: The Ways We Worship,* by Mary Pope Osborne (Knopf Books for Young Readers, 1996) ISBN 978-0679839309

27. *Sammy Spider's First Rosh Hashanah,* by Sylvia A. Rouss (Kar-Ben Publishing, 1996) ISBN 978-0929371993

28. *Under the Ramadan Moon,* by Sylvia Whitman (Albert Whitman & Company, 2011) ISBN 978-0807583050

29. *What Is Religion?,* by Bobbie Kalman (Crabtree Publishing Company, 2009) ISBN 978-0778746515

Websites and Other Resources

Student Resources

1. Egypt Game
   http://www.neok12.com/diagram/Ancient-Egypt-01.htm

2. Geography of Egypt
   http://kids.nationalgeographic.com/kids/places/find/egypt

3. World Religion Images (text may be too advanced for most students)
   http://www.uri.org/kids/world.htm

4. Ziggurats
   http://www.eduplace.com/kids/socsci/ca/books/bkf3/igraphics/
   AC_03_093_ziggurat/AC_03_093_ziggurat.html

Family Resources

5. Brooklyn Museum
   http://www.brooklynmuseum.org/exhibitions

6. Church of the Holy Sepulchre
   http://www.sacred-destinations.com/israel/
   jerusalem-holy-sepulchre-photos

7. Dome of the Rock
   http://www.sacred-destinations.com/israel/
   jerusalem-dome-of-the-rock-photos

8. Western Wall
   http://www.sacred-destinations.com/israel/
   jerusalem-western-wall-photos

9. World Religions for Teachers
   http://www.bbc.co.uk/schools/religion

Name _____

Directions: Draw a picture and/or write about what you have learned about each of these components of the civilizations of Mesopotamia and ancient Egypt.

	Mesopotamia	Ancient Egypt
Religion		
Leaders		
Writing		
Cities		
Farming		

Name _____

Directions: Draw a picture and/or write about what you have learned about each of these components of the civilizations of Mesopotamia.

	Mesopotamia
Religion	
Leaders	
Writing	
Cities	
Farming	

Name _____

Dear Family Member,

I hope you have enjoyed talking with your child about the ancient civilization of Mesopotamia. For the next several days, your child will be learning about another ancient civilization, ancient Egypt. S/he will learn about the importance of the Nile River for farming and the cities that grew where people settled. Your child will also learn about the development of a system of writing using hieroglyphs, the existence of leaders called pharaohs, and the importance of religion as key elements or components of a civilization. Your child will be able to compare this ancient civilization to Mesopotamia. Below are some suggestions for activities that you may do at home to reinforce what your child is learning about ancient Egypt.

1. Where Are We?

Have your child locate the continent of Africa and the country of Egypt on a world map or globe. (If you do not have a map, check one out from the library.) Talk about the geography of this area. (Sahara Desert, Nile River . . .)

2. Draw and Write

Have your child draw and/or write about what has been learned about ancient Egypt and then share the drawing with you. Ask questions to keep your child using the vocabulary learned at school.

3. Compare Civilizations

Compare/contrast the farming, cities, writing, leaders, and religion of ancient Mesopotamia and ancient Egypt. Talk about the importance of each of these components in both civilizations.

4. Read Aloud Each Day

It is very important that you read to your child each day. Please refer to the list of books and other resources sent home with the previous family letter, recommending resources related to ancient Egypt.

Be sure to let your child know how much you enjoy hearing about what s/he has been learning at school.

Name _____

Egyptian Hieroglyphs

Directions: Use these hieroglyphs to write your name and then some other words or a short message.

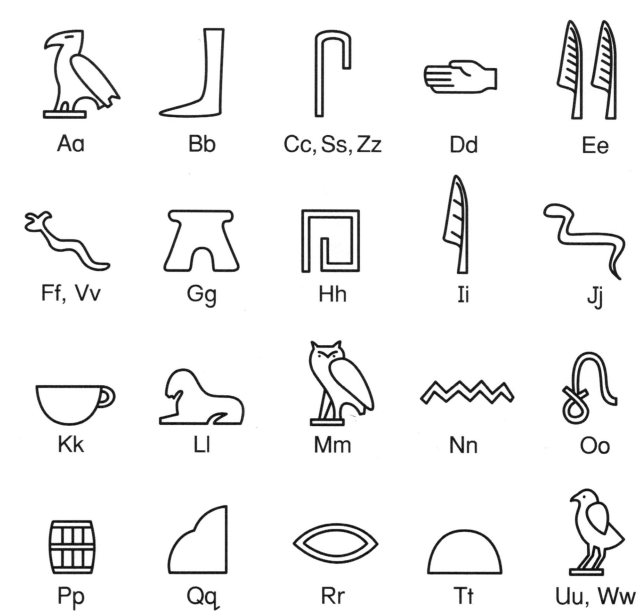

Aa	Bb	Cc, Ss, Zz	Dd	Ee
Ff, Vv	Gg	Hh	Ii	Jj
Kk	Ll	Mm	Nn	Oo
Pp	Qq	Rr	Tt	Uu, Ww

Name _____

Directions: Think about what you heard in the read-aloud to fill in the chart using words or sentences.

Somebody	
Wanted	
But	
So	
Then	

Name _____

Dear Family Member,

During the past several weeks, your child has been listening to read-alouds about the ancient civilizations and people of Mesopotamia and Egypt. They have learned that the ancient Mesopotamians and Egyptians worshiped many different gods. We have talked about how these beliefs influenced the daily lives of the ancient Mesopotamians and Egyptians and helped to shape their civilizations.

On _____, we will begin the remaining lessons in this unit of study. The read-alouds will extend what students have already learned about the ancient Mesopotamians' and Egyptians' belief in many gods. Lessons 13–16 will explain the historical changes that began to take place and how these ancient people developed new beliefs and practices focused on one God rather than many gods. These final read-alouds provide a historical introduction to the development of three world religions—Judaism, Christianity, and Islam—which are all characterized by a belief in a single God.

The Core Knowledge Language Arts program introduces students at various grade levels to the major world religions as part of their study of world history. The intent is to provide the vocabulary and context for understanding the many ways that the world religions have influenced ideas and events in history. It is important to understand that the religions your child will hear about in first grade—Judaism, Christianity, and Islam—are not being singled out or presented in any way that suggests the merits or correctness of specific religious beliefs.

The read-alouds in first grade focus on teaching students very basic similarities and differences among religions, and fostering an understanding and respect for those similarities and differences. The historical events and ideas leading to the development of each religion are presented in a balanced and respectful manner. If students have questions about the truth or "rightness" of any beliefs or religions, we will encourage them to discuss their questions with you at home, by saying, "People of different faiths believe different things to be true. These are questions you may want to talk about with your family and the adults at home."

The Core Knowledge Language Arts program's inclusion of world religions within the teaching of world history is comprehensive and balanced over the course of the elementary grades, presenting historical knowledge from around the world from ancient times to the present. The read-alouds about Judaism, Christianity, and Islam that your child will hear in first grade will be elaborated on in later grades. In addition, students in later grades will be introduced to other religions—such as Hinduism and Buddhism—as they learn about historical events in other parts of the world.

Please let us know if you have any questions or if you would like to see any of the read-alouds we are using.

Name _____

Directions: Draw a picture and/or write about what you have learned about each of these components of the civilizations of ancient Egypt.

Ancient Egypt
Religion
Leaders
Writing
Cities
Farming

Name _____

Three World Religions

	JUDAISM	CHRISTIANITY	ISLAM
NUMBER OF GODS			
NAME OF MAIN SHRINE IN JERUSALEM			
NAME OF KEY FIGURE(S)			
NAME OF FOLLOWERS			
SYMBOL OF FAITH			
BUILDING OF WORSHIP			
WORSHIP LEADER			
NAME OF HOLY BOOK			
IMPORTANT HOLIDAY			
INTERESTING FACT			

Name _____

1.

2.

3.

4.

5.

6.

7.

8.

9.

10.

Directions: Listen to your teacher's instructions.

11.

12.

13.

14.

15.

Name _____

1. M   Ⓔ

2. M   E

3. M   E

4. M   E

5. M   E

6. M   E

7.   M   E

8.   M   E

9.   M   E

10.   M   E

11.   M   E

12.   M   E

Name _____

Directions: Listen to the teacher read aloud the words in the left-hand and right-hand columns. Draw a line to match each religion with its symbol and leader.

1. Judaism

A. Jesus

2. Christianity

B. Moses

3. Islam

C. Muhammad

Name _____

Directions: Listen to the sentence read by the teacher. If the sentence is true for Judaism, circle the 'J' in the row. If the sentence is true for Christianity, circle the 'C' in the row. If the sentence is true for Islam, circle the 'I' in the row.

1. Ⓙ   C   I

2. J   C   I

3. J   C   I

4. J   C   I

5. J   C   I

6. J   C   I

7.   J   C   I

8.   J   C   I

9.   J   C   I

10.   J   C   I

11.   J   C   I

12.   J   C   I

CORE KNOWLEDGE LANGUAGE ARTS

SERIES EDITOR-IN-CHIEF
E. D. Hirsch, Jr.

PRESIDENT
Linda Bevilacqua

EDITORIAL STAFF
Carolyn Gosse, Senior Editor - Preschool
Khara Turnbull, Materials Development Manager
Michelle L. Warner, Senior Editor - Listening & Learning

Mick Anderson
Robin Blackshire
Maggie Buchanan
Paula Coyner
Sue Fulton
Sara Hunt
Erin Kist
Robin Luecke
Rosie McCormick
Cynthia Peng
Liz Pettit
Ellen Sadler
Deborah Samley
Diane Auger Smith
Sarah Zelinke

DESIGN AND GRAPHICS STAFF
Scott Ritchie, Creative Director

Kim Berrall
Michael Donegan
Liza Greene
Matt Leech
Bridget Moriarty
Lauren Pack

CONSULTING PROJECT MANAGEMENT SERVICES
ScribeConcepts.com

ADDITIONAL CONSULTING SERVICES
Ang Blanchette
Dorrit Green
Carolyn Pinkerton

ACKNOWLEDGMENTS

These materials are the result of the work, advice, and encouragement of numerous individuals over many years. Some of those singled out here already know the depth of our gratitude; others may be surprised to find themselves thanked publicly for help they gave quietly and generously for the sake of the enterprise alone. To helpers named and unnamed we are deeply grateful.

CONTRIBUTORS TO EARLIER VERSIONS OF THESE MATERIALS

Susan B. Albaugh, Kazuko Ashizawa, Nancy Braier, Kathryn M. Cummings, Michelle De Groot, Diana Espinal, Mary E. Forbes, Michael L. Ford, Ted Hirsch, Danielle Knecht, James K. Lee, Diane Henry Leipzig, Martha G. Mack, Liana Mahoney, Isabel McLean, Steve Morrison, Juliane K. Munson, Elizabeth B. Rasmussen, Laura Tortorelli, Rachael L. Shaw, Sivan B. Sherman, Miriam E. Vidaver, Catherine S. Whittington, Jeannette A. Williams

We would like to extend special recognition to Program Directors Matthew Davis and Souzanne Wright who were instrumental to the early development of this program.

SCHOOLS

We are truly grateful to the teachers, students, and administrators of the following schools for their willingness to field test these materials and for their invaluable advice: Capitol View Elementary, Challenge Foundation Academy (IN), Community Academy Public Charter School, Lake Lure Classical Academy, Lepanto Elementary School, New Holland Core Knowledge Academy, Paramount School of Excellence, Pioneer Challenge Foundation Academy, New York City PS 26R (The Carteret School), PS 30X (Wilton School), PS 50X (Clara Barton School), PS 96Q, PS 102X (Joseph O. Loretan), PS 104Q (The Bays Water), PS 214K (Michael Friedsam), PS 223Q (Lyndon B. Johnson School), PS 308K (Clara Cardwell), PS 333Q (Goldie Maple Academy), Sequoyah Elementary School, South Shore Charter Public School, Spartanburg Charter School, Steed Elementary School, Thomas Jefferson Classical Academy, Three Oaks Elementary, West Manor Elementary.

And a special thanks to the CKLA Pilot Coordinators Anita Henderson, Yasmin Lugo-Hernandez, and Susan Smith, whose suggestions and day-to-day support to teachers using these materials in their classrooms was critical.

Credits

Every effort has been taken to trace and acknowledge copyrights. The editors tender their apologies for any accidental infringement where copyright has proved untraceable. They would be pleased to insert the appropriate acknowledgment in any subsequent edition of this publication. Trademarks and trade names are shown in this publication for illustrative purposes only and are the property of their respective owners. The references to trademarks and trade names given herein do not affect their validity.

The Word Work exercises are based on the work of Beck, McKeown, and Kucan in Bringing Words to Life *(The Guilford Press, 2002).*

All photographs are used under license from Shutterstock, Inc. unless otherwise noted.

Expert Reviewers
James P. Allen, Benjamin Studevent-Hickman, Heather Warren, Patricia Wattenmaker

Writers
James Weiss, Catherine S. Whittington

Illustrators and Image Sources
Take-Home Icon: Core Knowledge Staff

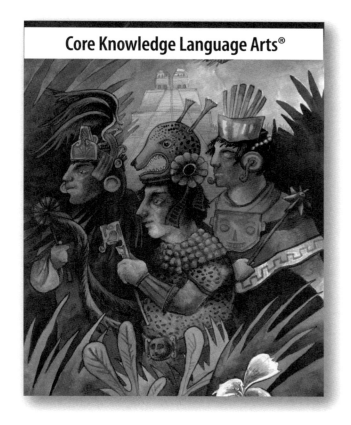

Core Knowledge Language Arts®

Domain 5: Early American Civilizations

Tell It Again!™ Workbook

Listening & Learning™ Strand

GRADE 1

Amplify learning.

Core Knowledge®

Dear Family Member,

During the next several days, your child will be learning about the Maya as part of a domain on early American civilizations. S/he will learn about the importance of farming and the cities that grew where people settled. Your child will also learn about the existence of leaders called kings as well as the importance of the stars and planets in the Mayan religion. Below are some suggestions for activities that you may do at home to reinforce what your child is learning about the Maya.

1. Where Are We?

Have your child locate the region where the Maya lived (Yucatán Peninsula and Guatemala) on a world map or globe. If you do not have a world map at home, you may be able to obtain one at your local library. Talk about the geography of this area. (rainforest, hot)

2. Draw and Write

Have your child draw and/or write about what s/he has learned about the Maya and then share the drawing with you. Ask questions to help your child use the vocabulary learned at school.

3. Compare Civilizations

Compare/contrast the farming, cities, leaders, and religion of the Maya relative to the present-day United States. Talk about the importance of each of these components in any civilization.

4. Sayings and Phrases: The More the Merrier

Your child has learned the saying "the more the merrier." Talk with your child about the meaning of this saying. (The more people who are involved in something, the more fun it will be.) Point out times when the saying applies in your daily life.

5. The Meaning of a Name

Your child has learned that the Maya named their children after names of plants or animals or even types of weather that were significant to them. Over the next week, talk with your child about the meaning of his or her name. Write his or her name on a note card, and then write the meaning of his or her name on the other side. Send the note card to school so that your child can share the meaning of his or her name with the rest of the class.

6. Read Aloud Each Day

It is very important that you read to your child each day. The local library has many books about Early American Civilizations, including books about the Maya and Mayan civilizations. A list of books and other resources relevant to this topic is attached to this letter.

Be sure to let your child know how much you enjoy hearing about what s/he has been learning at school.

Recommended Trade Books for Early American Civilizations

Note: I recommend that you preview all books before presenting them to determine whether the content is appropriate for your child. Because human sacrifice was a common practice in the Mayan, Aztec, and Incan cultures, a number of trade books mention this topic.

Trade Book List

1. *Aztec, Inca & Maya (Eyewitness Books),* by Elizabeth Baquedano (DK Children, 2011) ISBN 978-0756673208

2. *Early Civilizations of the Americas,* edited by E.D. Hirsch, Jr. (Pearson Learning, 2002) ISBN 978-0769050409

3. *Hands-On Latin America: Art Activities for All Ages*, by Yvonne Y. Merrill (Kits Publishing, 1998) ISBN 978-0964317710

4. *Maya, Aztecs and Incas,* by Oldrich Ruzicka and illustrated by Pavla Kleinova (Firefly Books, 2011) ISBN 978-1554079339

The Maya

5. *The Ancient Maya (True Books: Ancient Civilizations),* by Jackie Maloy (Children's Press, 2010) ISBN 978-0531252291

6. *Mario's Mayan Journey*, by Michelle McCunney (Mondo Publishing, 1997) ISBN 978-1572552036

7. *The Maya (True Books: American Indians),* by Stefanie Takacs (Children's Press, 2004) ISBN 978-0516279077

8. *Rain Player*, by David Wisniewski (Houghton Mifflin, 1995) ISBN 978-0395720837

The Aztec

9. *The Aztec (True Books: American Indians),* by Andrew Santella (Children's Press, 2003) ISBN 978-0516269733

10. *The Aztec Empire (True Books: Ancient Civilizations),* by Sunita Apte (Children's Press, 2010) ISBN 978-0531241080

11. *The Aztec Empire: Excavating the Past,* by Nicholas Saunders and Tony Allan (Heinemann-Raintree, 2005) ISBN 978-1403448392

The Inca

12. *The Inca (True Books: American Indians),* by Stefanie Takacs (Children's Press, 2004) ISBN 978-0516278230

13. *The Inca Empire (True Books: Ancient Civilizations),* by Sandra Newman (Children's Press, 2010) ISBN 978-0531252284

14. *Let's Go Up! Climbing Machu Picchu, Huayna Picchu And Putucusi,* by Tracy Foote (TracyTrends Publishing, 2009) ISBN 978-0981473703

15. *Lost City: The Discovery of Machu Picchu,* by Ted Lewin (Penguin Young Readers Group, 2012) ISBN 978-0142425800

16. *Machu Picchu with Code (Virtual Field Trips),* by Gillian Richardson, Heather Kissock (Weigl Publishers, 2012) ISBN 978-1619132566

Websites and Other Resources

Student Resources

1. Continents Game
   http://www.playkidsgames.com/games/continentNames/continentJig.htm

2. The Mayans
   http://www.mayankids.com

3. Archaeology Game
   http://www.history.org/kids/games/dirtDetective.cfm

4. American Museum of Natural History
   http://www.amnh.org

5. Memory Game
   http://www.mayankids.com/mmkgames/mkmemory.htm

Family Resources

6. Mayan Calendar
   http://www.webexhibits.org/calendars/calendar-mayan.html

Audio Resources

7. *Flutes Indiennes,* by Los Incas (Essential World Classics, 2012) ASIN B007TXUXT0

8. *Wasichakuy,* by Expresion (Tumi Records, 1998) ASIN B000007NU4

Name _____

Directions: Draw a picture and/or write about what you have learned about each of these components of the Maya, Aztec, and Inca civilizations.

	Maya	Aztec	Inca
Farming			
Cities			
Leaders			
Religion			

Name _____

Directions: Cut out the five pictures. Arrange the pictures in order to show the proper sequence of events in the legend. Once they have been sequenced, glue or tape the pictures onto a piece of paper.

Dear Family Member,

During the next several days, your child will be learning about two other ancient civilizations called the Aztec and Inca civilizations. S/he will learn about the importance of farming and the cities that grew where people settled. Your child will also learn about the existence of leaders called emperors. Below are some suggestions for activities that you may do at home to reinforce what your child is learning about the Aztec and Inca.

1. Where Are We?

Have your child locate the region where the Aztec lived (central Mexico, around Mexico City, north of the Maya) on a world map or globe. If you do not have a world map at home, you may be able to obtain one at your local library. Talk about the geography of this area. (swampland, lakes) Do the same for the Inca. The Inca lived in the Andes Mountains along the Pacific Ocean (present-day countries of Bolivia, Ecuador, Argentina, Chile, and Peru).

2. Draw and Write

Have your child draw and/or write about what has been learned about the Aztec and Inca and then share the drawing with you. Ask questions to help your child use the vocabulary learned at school.

3. Compare Civilizations

Compare/contrast the farming, cities, leaders, and religion of the Aztec and Inca relative to the present-day United States. Talk about the importance of each of these components in any civilization.

4. Read Aloud Each Day

It is very important that you read to your child each day. The local library has many books about Early American civilizations, including books about the Aztec and Inca and their civilizations. Refer to the list of books and other resources relevant to this topic that was sent home with the previous family letter.

Be sure to let your child know how much you enjoy hearing about what s/he has been learning at school.

Name _____

Directions: Listen to your teacher's instructions.

1.

2.

3.

4.

5.

6.

7.

8.

9.

10.

11.

12.

13.

14.

15.

Name _____

Directions: Listen to the sentence read by the teacher. If the sentence is true for the Maya civilization, circle the 'M' in the row. If the sentence is true for the Aztec civilization, circle the 'A' in the row. If the sentence is true for the Inca civilization, circle the 'I' in the row. If the sentence is true for all civilizations, circle the 'M,' the 'A,' and the 'I' in the row.

1.   M   A   I

2.   M   A   I

3.   M   A   I

4.   M   A   I

5.   M   A   I

6.   M   A   I

7.   M   A   I

8.   M   A   I

9.   M   A   I

10.   M   A   I

CORE KNOWLEDGE LANGUAGE ARTS

SERIES EDITOR-IN-CHIEF
E. D. Hirsch, Jr.

PRESIDENT
Linda Bevilacqua

EDITORIAL STAFF
Carolyn Gosse, Senior Editor - Preschool
Khara Turnbull, Materials Development Manager
Michelle L. Warner, Senior Editor - Listening & Learning

Mick Anderson
Robin Blackshire
Maggie Buchanan
Paula Coyner
Sue Fulton
Sara Hunt
Erin Kist
Robin Luecke
Rosie McCormick
Cynthia Peng
Liz Pettit
Ellen Sadler
Deborah Samley
Diane Auger Smith
Sarah Zelinke

DESIGN AND GRAPHICS STAFF
Scott Ritchie, Creative Director

Kim Berrall
Michael Donegan
Liza Greene
Matt Leech
Bridget Moriarty
Lauren Pack

CONSULTING PROJECT MANAGEMENT SERVICES
ScribeConcepts.com

ADDITIONAL CONSULTING SERVICES
Ang Blanchette
Dorrit Green
Carolyn Pinkerton

ACKNOWLEDGMENTS

These materials are the result of the work, advice, and encouragement of numerous individuals over many years. Some of those singled out here already know the depth of our gratitude; others may be surprised to find themselves thanked publicly for help they gave quietly and generously for the sake of the enterprise alone. To helpers named and unnamed we are deeply grateful.

CONTRIBUTORS TO EARLIER VERSIONS OF THESE MATERIALS
Susan B. Albaugh, Kazuko Ashizawa, Nancy Braier, Kathryn M. Cummings, Michelle De Groot, Diana Espinal, Mary E. Forbes, Michael L. Ford, Ted Hirsch, Danielle Knecht, James K. Lee, Diane Henry Leipzig, Martha G. Mack, Liana Mahoney, Isabel McLean, Steve Morrison, Juliane K. Munson, Elizabeth B. Rasmussen, Laura Tortorelli, Rachael L. Shaw, Sivan B. Sherman, Miriam E. Vidaver, Catherine S. Whittington, Jeannette A. Williams

We would like to extend special recognition to Program Directors Matthew Davis and Souzanne Wright who were instrumental to the early development of this program.

SCHOOLS
We are truly grateful to the teachers, students, and administrators of the following schools for their willingness to field test these materials and for their invaluable advice: Capitol View Elementary, Challenge Foundation Academy (IN), Community Academy Public Charter School, Lake Lure Classical Academy, Lepanto Elementary School, New Holland Core Knowledge Academy, Paramount School of Excellence, Pioneer Challenge Foundation Academy, New York City PS 26R (The Carteret School), PS 30X (Wilton School), PS 50X (Clara Barton School), PS 96Q, PS 102X (Joseph O. Loretan), PS 104Q (The Bays Water), PS 214K (Michael Friedsam), PS 223Q (Lyndon B. Johnson School), PS 308K (Clara Cardwell), PS 333Q (Goldie Maple Academy), Sequoyah Elementary School, South Shore Charter Public School, Spartanburg Charter School, Steed Elementary School, Thomas Jefferson Classical Academy, Three Oaks Elementary, West Manor Elementary.

And a special thanks to the CKLA Pilot Coordinators Anita Henderson, Yasmin Lugo-Hernandez, and Susan Smith, whose suggestions and day-to-day support to teachers using these materials in their classrooms was critical.

CREDITS

Every effort has been taken to trace and acknowledge copyrights. The editors tender their apologies for any accidental infringement where copyright has proved untraceable. They would be pleased to insert the appropriate acknowledgment in any subsequent edition of this publication. Trademarks and trade names are shown in this publication for illustrative purposes only and are the property of their respective owners. The references to trademarks and trade names given herein do not affect their validity.

The Word Work exercises are based on the work of Beck, McKeown, and Kucan in Bringing Words to Life *(The Guilford Press, 2002).*

All photographs are used under license from Shutterstock, Inc. unless otherwise noted.

EXPERT REVIEWER
Marilyn A. Masson, Michael E. Smith

WRITERS
Rachel L. Shaw, James Weiss, Catherine S. Whittington

ILLUSTRATORS AND IMAGE SOURCES
Take Home Icon: Core Knowledge Staff; 5B-1: Anthony Holden; 5B-1 Answer Key: Anthony Holden

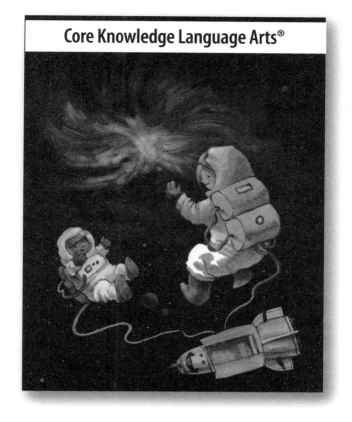

Domain 6: Astronomy
Tell It Again!™ Workbook

Listening & Learning™ Strand
GRADE 1

Amplify learning.

Core Knowledge®

Name _____

My Astronomy Journal

By _____

Directions:

Write your name on the blank line.

Lesson 1: Sketch your observations of the sky in daytime.

Lesson 3: Sketch what the sky looks like at dusk.

Lesson 7: Sketch a spacecraft of your own design.

Lesson 8: Sketch yourself as an astronaut.

Dear Family Member,

Over the next few weeks, your child will be learning about astronomy. Your child will learn about the sun, the moon, the stars, and the eight planets in our solar system. Your child will also learn about space exploration, including the first astronauts to land on the moon.

In the next few days, we will focus our study of astronomy on the sun, the moon, and the stars. The most powerful way you can help support your child's learning about astronomy is to take him or her outside to observe the sky. Below are some suggestions for ways you can make his/her study of astronomy even more meaningful and fun, and some words s/he is learning that relate to each activity.

1. Sunrise or Sunset

Your child is learning that the earth orbits or revolves around the sun. S/he is also learning that even though it looks like the sun moves across the sky each day, it is actually the earth spinning on its axis that causes day and night. Your child will learn about the earth's atmosphere, and how it causes the sky to change colors, especially at sunrise and sunset. Go outside with your child at dawn to observe the sunrise, or at dusk to observe the sunset.

Words to use: *dusk, dawn, atmosphere, revolve, horizon*

2. Stargazing

In a few days your child will learn about the stars and the constellations. Take your child out in the evening to observe the stars. The Big and Little Dipper are part of the Big Bear constellation. S/he will learn to recognize the dippers and Polaris (the North Star). Together with your child, try to identify these groups of stars in the night sky. You may wish to obtain a book from the library on constellations to guide your observations.

Words to use: *constellation, star, telescope, outer space, meteor*

3. Phases of the Moon

Your child will learn about the moon and how it orbits the earth, reflecting the sun's light. S/he will also learn to recognize its four phases: the new moon, the crescent moon, the half moon, and the full moon. Look for the moon every few days and talk with your child about how much of it is visible in the sky.

Words to use: *crescent, full, reflecting, orbit, craters, man in the moon*

4. Read Aloud Each Day

It is very important that you read to your child each day. The local library has many books on astronomy and a list of books and other resources relevant to this topic is attached to this letter.

Be sure to let your child know how much you enjoy hearing about what s/he has been learning at school.

Name _____

Recommended Trade Books for Astronomy

1. *Astronomy* (DK Eyewitness Books), by Kristin Lippincott (DK Children, 2008) ISBN 978-0756637675

2. *Exploring the Solar System,* by Mary Kay Carson (Chicago Review Press, 2008) ISBN 978-1556527159

3. *Find the Constellations*, by H. A. Rey (Houghton Mifflin Books for Children, 2008) ISBN 978-0547131788

4. *Find Out About Astronomy,* by Robin Kerrod (Armadillo, 2012) ISBN 978-1843228684

5. *The Magic School Bus: Lost in the Solar System*, by Joanna Cole and illustrated by Bruce Degen (Scholastic Inc., 1992) ISBN 978-0590414296

6. *Midnight on the Moon (Magic Tree House, No. 8)*, by Mary Pope Osborne and Sal Murdocca (Random House Books for Young Readers, 1996) ISBN 978-0679863748

7. *The Moon Seems to Change*, by Franklyn M. Branley and illustrated by Barbara and Ed Emberley (HarperCollins, 1987) ISBN 978-0064450652

8. *National Geographic Readers: Planets,* by Elizabeth Carney (National Geographic Children's Books, 2012) ISBN 978-1426310362

9. *National Geographic Little Kids First Big Book of Space,* by Catherine D. Hughes and illustrated by David A. Aguilar (National Geographic Children's Books, 2012) ISBN 978-1426310140

10. *Once Upon a Starry Night: A Book of Constellations*, by Jacqueline Mitton and illustrated by Christina Balit (National Geographic Children's Books, 2009) ISBN 978-1426303913 (**Note:** This book's beautiful illustrations can help students imagine what the constellations look like when they look up at the stars. The myths/ text, however, is not recommended for first grade.)

11. *Our Solar System*, by Seymour Simon (Collins, 2007) ISBN 978-0061140082

12. *Planets: A Solar System Stickerbook*, by Ellen Hasbrouck and illustrated by Scott McDougall (Little Simon, 2001) ISBN 978-0689844140

13. *Stargazers*, by Gail Gibbons (Holiday House, 1999) ISBN 978-0823415076

14. *Starry Sky,* by Kate Hayden (DK Children, 2006) ISBN 978-0756619596

15. *Sun Up*, Sun Down, by Gail Gibbons (Voyager Books, 1987) ISBN 978-0152827823

16. *What Makes Day and Night*, by Franklyn M. Branley and illustrated by Arthur Dorros (HarperCollins, 1986) ISBN 978-0064450508

17. *Wynken, Blynken, and Nod*, by Eugene W. Field and illustrated by Giselle Potter (Schwartz & Wade, 2008) ISBN 978-0375841965

Note: Please remember to tell students that not very long ago, students in school were taught that there were nine planets in the solar system, including Pluto. However, in 2006, astronomers decided to categorize Pluto as a dwarf planet, so there are now eight major planets. If you choose additional books to read aloud, be sure to include the phrase *dwarf planet* when referring to Pluto. Remember also that there are still many excellent astronomy books in print that classify Pluto as a planet, but are otherwise informative trade books.

Websites and Other Resources

Student Resources

1. Interactive Earth Rotation
   http://www.bbc.co.uk/schools/scienceclips/ages/9_10/earth_sun_moon.shtml

2. NASA Kids' Club
   http://www.nasa.gov/audience/forkids/kidsclub/flash/index.html

3. National Geographic Space Activities and Photos
   http://kids.nationalgeographic.com/kids/photos/space-shuttles/#/columbia-launch-gpn-2000-000756_14481_600x450.jpg

4. PBS Game on Outer Space
   http://pbskids.org/martha/games/socksinspace/index.html

Family Resources

5. American Museum of Natural History Resources on Space
   http://www.amnh.org/content/search?SearchText=space&x=0&y=0

6. Photographs from the Hubble Space Telescope
   http://hubblesite.org/gallery/album/entire/npp/all/

Name _____

Directions: The pictures show four different phases of the moon. Write the number "1" on the line below the new moon. Write the number "2" below the crescent moon. Write the number "3" below the half moon. Write the number "4" below the full moon.

_____

_____

Astronomy

Dear Family Member,

Over the next few days, your child will be continuing his/her study of astronomy. Your child has now learned about the sun and the stars, and has begun to learn about the moon. In the next few days, our class will focus our study on space exploration and the planets in the solar system. The most powerful way you can help support your child's learning about astronomy is to continue taking him/her outside to observe the sky. Below are some additional suggestions for activities, and some words s/he is or will be learning that relate to each activity.

1. Name the Planets

Your child will be learning about the eight planets in our solar system: Mercury, Venus, Earth, Mars, Jupiter, Saturn, Uranus, and Neptune. S/he will also learn that Pluto was once considered a planet, but in 2006 was categorized as a dwarf planet. When you were in school, you may have learned a mnemonic to remember the names of the (then) nine planets, such as "My Very Educated Mother Just Served Us Nine Pizzas." Write a new mnemonic with your child to help him/her remember the list of eight names above.

2. Make a Model

Work with your child to use play dough or modeling clay to create models of the sun and the planets. Lay the models on a black piece of paper, and draw chalk lines to represent orbits. Alternatively, work with your child to paint or draw a diagram of the solar system on a piece of paper.

3. Planet Earth

Your child has learned that our home, Earth, is a planet that it is in constant motion. It is difficult to believe that we are living on a moving sphere when the land beneath our feet seems still and flat. Explore a globe with your child and help him/her understand that it represents the planet Earth. Locate the United States and other countries your child knows about. Talk about the poles and the axis. Observe how much of the planet is covered by the continents and how much is covered by the oceans.

4. Astronauts for a Day

Your child will learn about spacecraft and astronauts in the coming days. If the thought of space travel captures your child's imagination, pretend to be astronauts together. Dress up in spacesuits and helmets. Using furniture or boxes, assemble a spacecraft. Countdown to launch, hurtle through space propelled by a rocket, and pretend to land on the moon or another planet.

5. Read Aloud Each Day

It is very important that you read to your child each day. Please refer to the list of books and other resources sent home with the previous family letter, recommending resources related to astronomy.

Be sure to let your child know how much you enjoy hearing about what s/he has been learning at school.

Name _____

Directions: The pictures show the earth, the sun, and the moon. If what I read to you describes something about the earth, circle the first picture in the row. If what I read to you describes something about the sun, circle the second picture in the row. If what I read to you describes something about the moon, circle the last picture in the row.

	Earth	Sun	Moon
1.			
2.			
3.			
4.			
5.			

Name _____

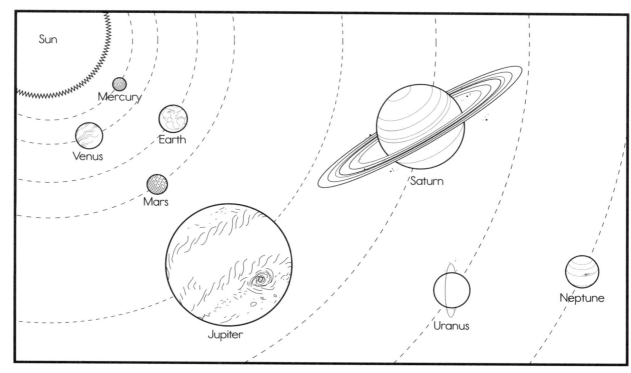

Directions: Read and answer each question appropriately using the diagram. You may wish to color the diagram to reflect what you know about the colors of certain planets in the solar system.

1. How many planets orbit the sun?

    _____

2. Which planet is closest to the sun?

    _____

3. Is Mars larger or smaller than Earth?

    _____

4. Which planet has a few rings around it?

    _____

Name _____

1.

2.

3.

4.

5.

6.

7.

8.

9.

10.

Directions: Listen to your teacher's instructions.

Name _____

Directions: Listen to the following sentences about these celestial bodies. Next to the number of the sentence I have read, you will notice four names. You will notice that the first three names are always the same. Let's read them together: "sun, moon, Earth." You will also notice that the last name is usually different. I will read the four choices to you after I read each sentence. Circle the name of the appropriate celestial body being talked about in each sentence:

1.   Sun   Moon   Earth   Neptune

2.   Sun   Moon   Earth   Saturn

3.   Sun   Moon   Earth   Mercury

4.   Sun   Moon   Earth   Mars

5.   Sun   Moon   Earth   Jupiter

6.   Sun   Moon   Earth   Uranus

7.   Sun   Moon   Earth   Venus

8.   Sun   Moon   Earth   Mercury

9.	Sun	Moon	Earth	Saturn
10.	Sun	Moon	Earth	Jupiter
11.	Sun	Moon	Earth	Mars
12.	Sun	Moon	Earth	Venus
13.	Sun	Moon	Earth	Uranus
14.	Sun	Moon	Earth	Neptune
15.	Sun	Moon	Earth	Mercury

CORE KNOWLEDGE LANGUAGE ARTS

SERIES EDITOR-IN-CHIEF
E. D. Hirsch, Jr.

PRESIDENT
Linda Bevilacqua

EDITORIAL STAFF
Carolyn Gosse, Senior Editor - Preschool
Khara Turnbull, Materials Development Manager
Michelle L. Warner, Senior Editor - Listening & Learning

Mick Anderson
Robin Blackshire
Maggie Buchanan
Paula Coyner
Sue Fulton
Sara Hunt
Erin Kist
Robin Luecke
Rosie McCormick
Cynthia Peng
Liz Pettit
Ellen Sadler
Deborah Samley
Diane Auger Smith
Sarah Zelinke

DESIGN AND GRAPHICS STAFF
Scott Ritchie, Creative Director

Kim Berrall
Michael Donegan
Liza Greene
Matt Leech
Bridget Moriarty
Lauren Pack

CONSULTING PROJECT MANAGEMENT SERVICES
ScribeConcepts.com

ADDITIONAL CONSULTING SERVICES
Ang Blanchette
Dorrit Green
Carolyn Pinkerton

ACKNOWLEDGMENTS

These materials are the result of the work, advice, and encouragement of numerous individuals over many years. Some of those singled out here already know the depth of our gratitude; others may be surprised to find themselves thanked publicly for help they gave quietly and generously for the sake of the enterprise alone. To helpers named and unnamed we are deeply grateful.

CONTRIBUTORS TO EARLIER VERSIONS OF THESE MATERIALS

Susan B. Albaugh, Kazuko Ashizawa, Nancy Braier, Kathryn M. Cummings, Michelle De Groot, Diana Espinal, Mary E. Forbes, Michael L. Ford, Ted Hirsch, Danielle Knecht, James K. Lee, Diane Henry Leipzig, Martha G. Mack, Liana Mahoney, Isabel McLean, Steve Morrison, Juliane K. Munson, Elizabeth B. Rasmussen, Laura Tortorelli, Rachael L. Shaw, Sivan B. Sherman, Miriam E. Vidaver, Catherine S. Whittington, Jeannette A. Williams

We would like to extend special recognition to Program Directors Matthew Davis and Souzanne Wright who were instrumental to the early development of this program.

SCHOOLS

We are truly grateful to the teachers, students, and administrators of the following schools for their willingness to field test these materials and for their invaluable advice: Capitol View Elementary, Challenge Foundation Academy (IN), Community Academy Public Charter School, Lake Lure Classical Academy, Lepanto Elementary School, New Holland Core Knowledge Academy, Paramount School of Excellence, Pioneer Challenge Foundation Academy, New York City PS 26R (The Carteret School), PS 30X (Wilton School), PS 50X (Clara Barton School), PS 96Q, PS 102X (Joseph O. Loretan), PS 104Q (The Bays Water), PS 214K (Michael Friedsam), PS 223Q (Lyndon B. Johnson School), PS 308K (Clara Cardwell), PS 333Q (Goldie Maple Academy), Sequoyah Elementary School, South Shore Charter Public School, Spartanburg Charter School, Steed Elementary School, Thomas Jefferson Classical Academy, Three Oaks Elementary, West Manor Elementary.

And a special thanks to the CKLA Pilot Coordinators Anita Henderson, Yasmin Lugo-Hernandez, and Susan Smith, whose suggestions and day-to-day support to teachers using these materials in their classrooms was critical.

CREDITS

EXPERT REVIEWER
Charles R. Tolbert

WRITERS
Michael L. Ford

ILLUSTRATORS AND IMAGE SOURCES
Take Home Icon: Core Knowledge Staff; 5B-1: Shutterstock; 5B-1 Answer Key: Shutterstock; PP-1: Shutterstock; PP-1 Answer Key: Shutterstock